HEINRICH HOFMANN
17 MISCELLANEOUS PIECE_

Edited by Thomas A. Johnson

THE ASSOCIATED BOARD OF
THE ROYAL SCHOOLS OF MUSIC

INTRODUCTION

Heinrich Karl Johann Hofmann, the German composer and pianist, was born in Berlin in 1842 and died in 1902 at Gross-Tabarz, Thuringia. At the age of nine he became a cathedral chorister, and at fifteen he entered Theodor Kullak's Neue Akademie der Tonkunst in Berlin. On leaving the Akademie, he started to teach and play the piano professionally, and he first attracted attention as a composer in 1869 with his comic opera, *Cartouche*. The subsequent successes of his *Ungarische Suite* and *Frithjof-Symphonie* encouraged him to devote his whole time to composition, but the popularity of his orchestral works did not outlast the century.

He is better known today for his smaller-scale works for chamber groups and for the keyboard. Some of his easier piano pieces are included in this album, and they have been taken from the following sources:

Albumblätter, Op.11 (Novello, London)
Nachklänge, Part II, Op.37 (Novello, London)
Skizzen, Op.77 (Carl Rühle, Leipzig)
Lose Blätter, Op.85 (Challier, Berlin)
Stimmungsbilder, Op.87 (Steingraber, Leipzig)

Certain inconsistencies in marks of expression and articulation have been regularised, and others have been added. One or two obvious misprints have been corrected. Fingering has been revised, and some pedalling indications have been included. At the end of each piece a metronome mark has been suggested, but it is no way authoritative or binding.

THOMAS A. JOHNSON
Neston, South Wirral 1985

Melodie

H. HOFMANN, Op.77 No.5

Am Abend
In the Evening

Op. 88 No. 2

AB1904

[♩.=c.84]

Ländler
Country Waltz

Op.77 No.3

Allegro moderato

[♩=c.116]

Waldvöglein
Little Wood-bird

Op.77 No.15

AB1904

Minnelied
Lyric Song

Op. 88 No. 7

[♪ =c.126]

Scherzo

Op.77 No.7

[♩ =c.72]

Gavotte

Op.88 No.1

Ped. come prima

[♩ =c.69]

Lied
Song

Op.85 No.2

[♩ =c.92]

Elfen
Elves

Op.77 No.17

Presto e leggiero

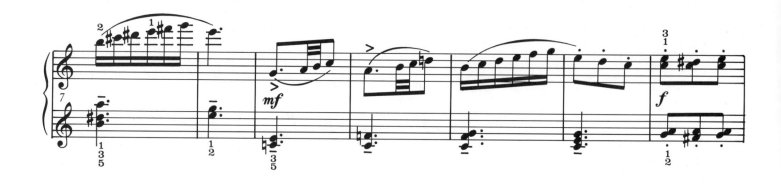

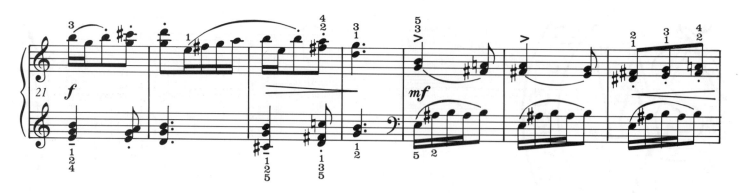

[♩.=c.69]

Notturno
Nocturne

Op. 88 No. 3

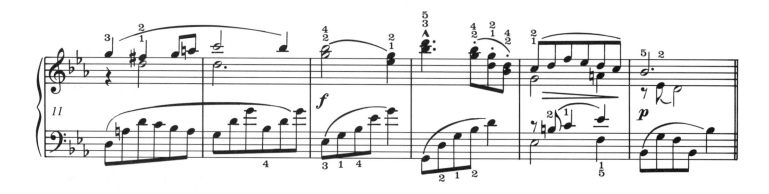

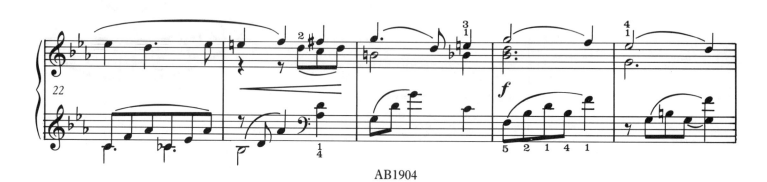

[♩ = c.100]

Schlaf ein!
Go to Sleep!

Op.77 No.9

Elegie

Op.77 No.2

[♩=c.54]

Albumblatt – In Mai
Album Leaf – In May

Op.11 Bk.1 No.2

[♩ = c.72]

Schelm
Rogue

Op.77 No.1

[♩ =c.112]

Auf dem See
On the Lake

Op.77 No.12

[♩.=c.80]

Zur Laute
To the Lute

Op. 37 No. 1

Am Giessbach
By the Mountain Torrent

Op. 37 No.2

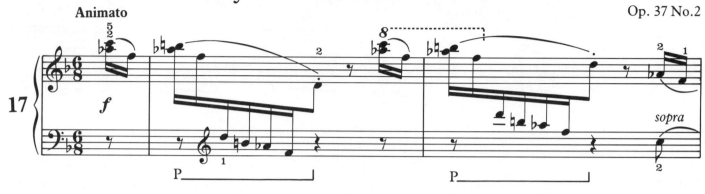

Reproduced and printed by
Halstan & Co. Ltd., Amersham, Bucks., England

[♩.=c.60]

Smooth Jazz Guitar Solos

Wise Publications
London/New York/Paris/Sydney/Copenhagen/Madrid/Tokyo

Exclusive distributors:
Music Sales Limited, 8/9 Frith Street, London W1D 3JB, England.
Music Sales Pty Limited, 120 Rothschild Avenue, Rosebery, NSW 2018, Australia.

Order No. AM967978
ISBN 0-7119-8556-1
This book © Copyright 1997, 2000 by Wise Publications
(Previously published as Jazz Cafe for Guitar Tablature)

Compiled by Peter Evans
Music arranged by Andy Jones
Music processed by Digital Music Art
Cover design by Chloë Alexander
Cover photograph courtesy of SuperStock
Printed in the United Kingdom

Your Guarantee of Quality
As publishers, we strive to produce every book to the highest commercial standards.
This the book has been carefully designed to minimise awkward page turns and to
make playing from it a real pleasure.
Particular care has been given to specifying acid-free, neutral-sized paper made from
pulps which have not been elemental chlorine bleached. This pulp is from farmed
sustainable forests and was produced with special regard for the environment.
Throughout, the printing and binding have been planned to ensure a sturdy, attractive
publication which should give years of enjoyment. If your copy fails to meet our high
standards, please inform us and we will gladly replace it.

Music Sales' complete catalogue describes thousands of titles and is available in full
colour sections by subject, direct from Music Sales Limited. Please state your areas of
interest and send a cheque/postal order for £1.50 for postage to: Music Sales Limited,
Newmarket Road, Bury St. Edmunds, Suffolk IP33 3YB.

www.musicsales.com

CONTENTS

Guitar Tablature Explained

Guitar music can be notated three different ways: on a musical stave, in tablature, and in rhythm slashes

RHYTHM SLASHES are written above the stave. Strum chords in the rhythm indicated. Round noteheads indicate single notes.

THE MUSICAL STAVE shows pitches and rhythms and is divided by lines into bars. Pitches are named after the first seven letters of the alphabet.

TABLATURE graphically represents the guitar fingerboard. Each horizontal line represents a string, and each number represents a fret.

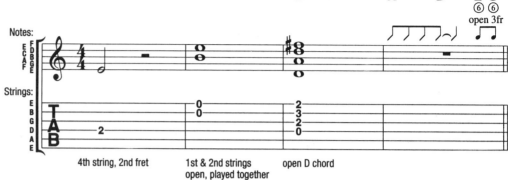

4th string, 2nd fret

1st & 2nd strings open, played together

open D chord

definitions for special guitar notation

SEMI-TONE BEND: Strike the note and bend up a semi-tone (1/2 step).

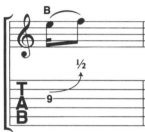

WHOLE-TONE BEND: Strike the note and bend up a whole-tone (whole step).

GRACE NOTE BEND: Strike the note and bend as indicated. Play the first note as quickly as possible.

QUARTER-TONE BEND: Strike the note and bend up a 1/4 step.

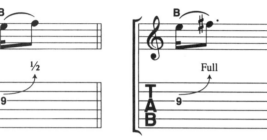
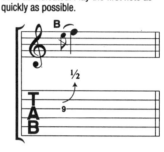
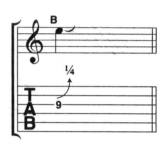

BEND & RELEASE: Strike the note and bend up as indicated, then release back to the original note.

COMPOUND BEND & RELEASE: Strike the note and bend up and down in the rhythm indicated.

PRE-BEND: Bend the note as indicated, then strike it.

PRE-BEND & RELEASE: Bend the note as indicated. Strike it and release the note back to the original pitch.

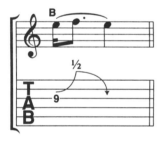
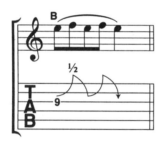

UNISON BEND: Strike the two notes simultaneously and bend the lower note up to the pitch of the higher.

BEND & RESTRIKE: Strike the note and bend as indicated then restrike the string where the symbol occurs.

BEND, HOLD AND RELEASE: Same as bend and release but hold the bend for the duration of the tie.

BEND AND TAP: Bend the note as indicated and tap the higher fret while still holding the bend.

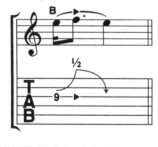
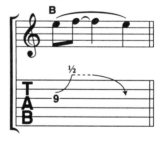
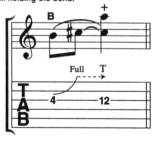

VIBRATO: The string is vibrated by rapidly bending and releasing the note with the fretting hand.

HAMMER-ON: Strike the first (lower) note with one finger, then sound the higher note (on the same string) with another finger by fretting it without picking.

PULL-OFF: Place both fingers on the notes to be sounded, Strike the first note and without picking, pull the finger off to sound the second (lower) note.

LEGATO SLIDE (GLISS): Strike the first note and then slide the same fret-hand finger up or down to the second note. The second note is not struck.

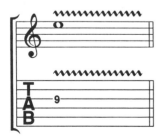

NOTE: The speed of any bend is indicated by the music notation and tempo.

4

SHIFT SLIDE (GLISS & RESTRIKE): Same as legato slide, except the second note is struck.

TRILL: Very rapidly alternate between the notes indicated by continuously hammering on and pulling off.

TAPPING: Hammer ("tap") the fret indicated with the pick-hand index or middle finger and pull off to the note fretted by the fret hand.

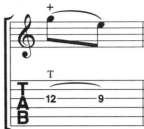

PICK SCRAPE: The edge of the pick is rubbed down (or up) the string, producing a scratchy sound.

MUFFLED STRINGS: A percussive sound is produced by laying the fret hand across the string(s) without depressing, and striking them with the pick hand.

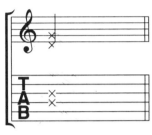

NATURAL HARMONIC: Strike the note while the fret-hand lightly touches the string directly over the fret indicated.

PINCH HARMONIC: The note is fretted normally and a harmonic is produced by adding the edge of the thumb or the tip of the index finger of the pick hand to the normal pick attack.

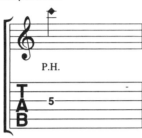

HARP HARMONIC: The note is fretted normally and a harmonic is produced by gently resting the pick hand's index finger directly above the indicated fret (in parentheses) while the pick hand's thumb or pick assists by plucking the appropriate string.

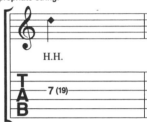

PALM MUTING: The note is partially muted by the pick hand lightly touching the string(s) just before the bridge.

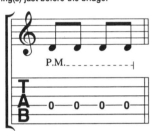

RAKE: Drag the pick across the strings indicated with a single motion.

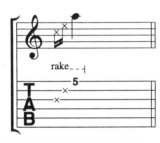

TREMOLO PICKING: The note is picked as rapidly and continuously as possible.

ARPEGGIATE: Play the notes of the chord indicated by quickly rolling them from bottom to top.

SWEEP PICKING: Rhythmic downstroke and/or upstroke motion across the strings.

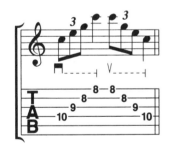

VIBRATO DIVE BAR AND RETURN: The pitch of the note or chord is dropped a specific number of steps (in rhythm) then returned to the original pitch.

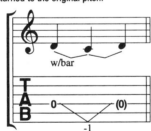

VIBRATO BAR SCOOP: Depress the bar just before striking the note, then quickly release the bar.

VIBRATO BAR DIP: Strike the note and then immediately drop a specific number of steps, then release back to the original pitch.

additional musical definitions

(accent) • Accentuate note (play it louder).

(accent) • Accentuate note with great intensity.

(staccato) • Shorten time value of note.

◼ • Downstroke

∨ • Upstroke

D.%. al Coda

D.C. al Fine

tacet

• Go back to the sign (%), then play until the bar marked *To Coda* ⊕ then skip to the section marked ⊕ *Coda*.

• Go back to the beginning of the song and play until the bar marked *Fine* (end).

• Instrument is silent (drops out).

• Repeat bars between signs.

• When a repeated section has different endings, play the first ending only the first time and the second ending only the second time.

NOTE: Tablature numbers in parentheses mean:
1. The note is sustained, but a new articulation (such as hammer on or slide) begins.
2. A note may be fretted but not necessarily played.

Fly Me To The Moon (In Other Words)

Words and Music by Bart Howard

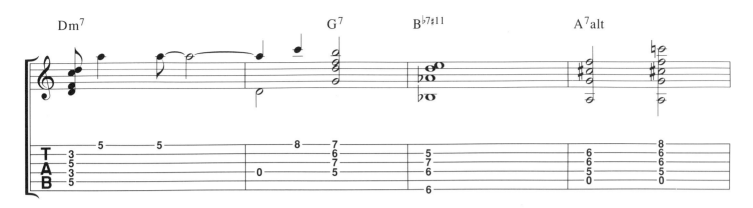

D.C. al Coda

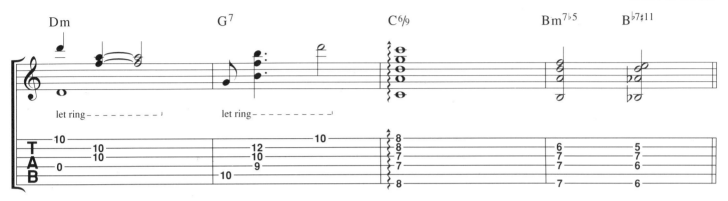

Chelsea Bridge

by Billy Strayhorn

The Girl From Ipanema (Garota De Ipanema)

Original Words by Vinicius De Moraes. English Lyric by Norman Gimbel.

Music by Antonio Carlos Jobim

Here's That Rainy Day

Words and Music by Johnny Burke & Jimmy Van Heusen

Honeysuckle Rose

Music by Thomas 'Fats' Waller. Words by Andy Razaf

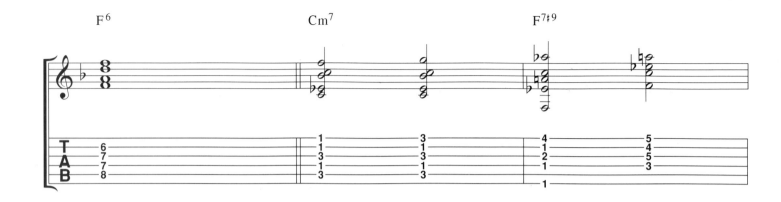

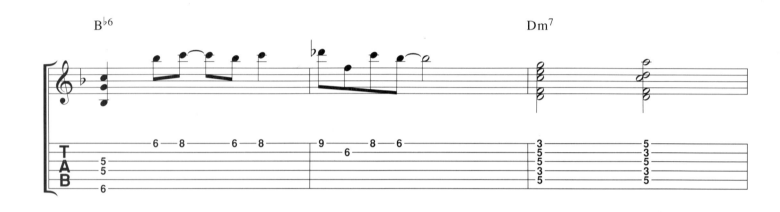

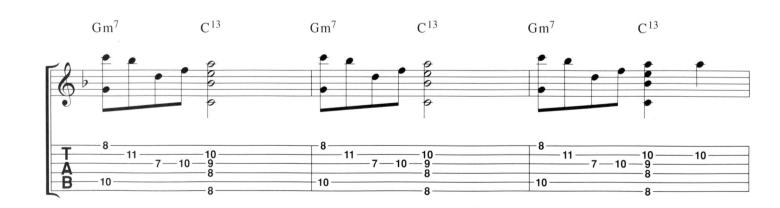

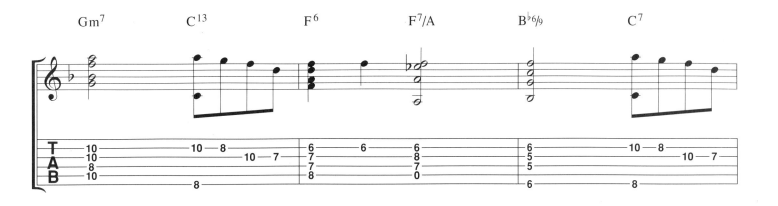

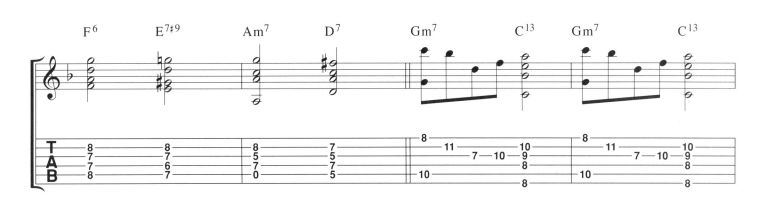

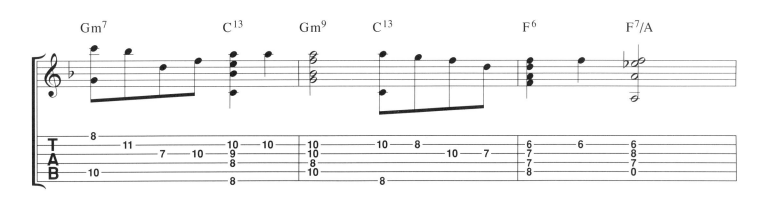

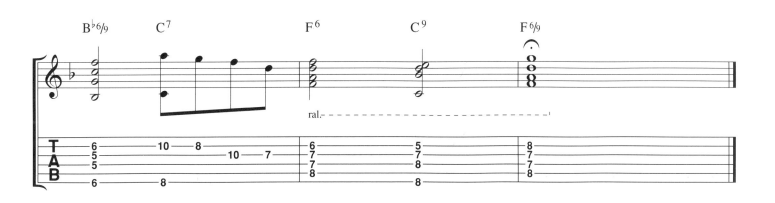

I'll Remember April

Words and Music by Don Raye, Gene de Paul & Patricia Johnson

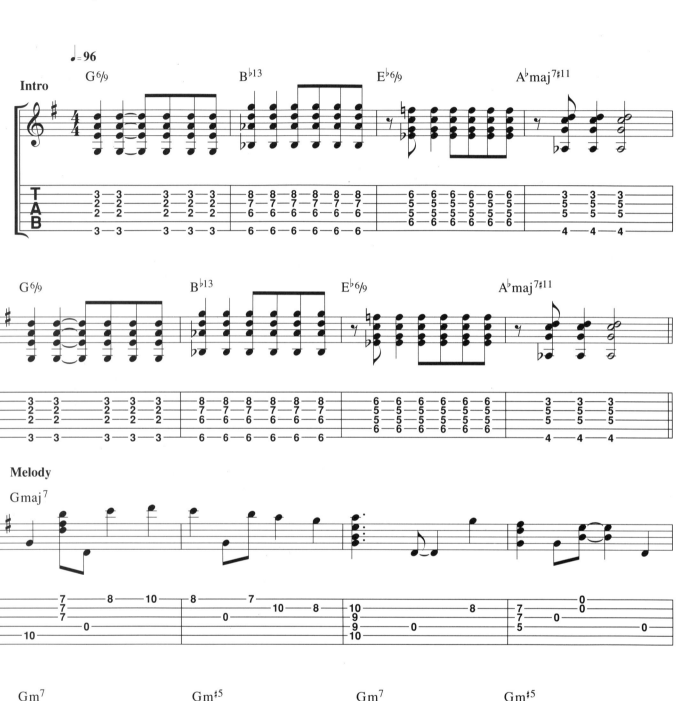

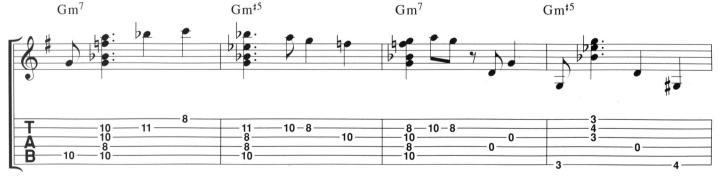

To Coda ⊕

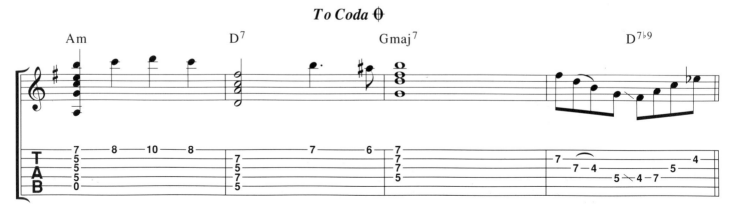

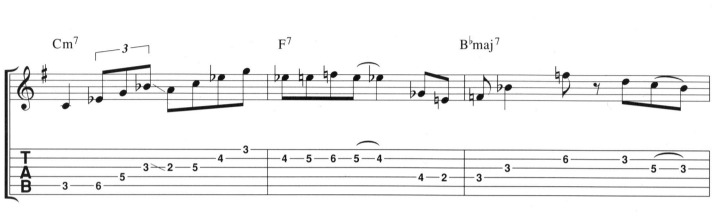

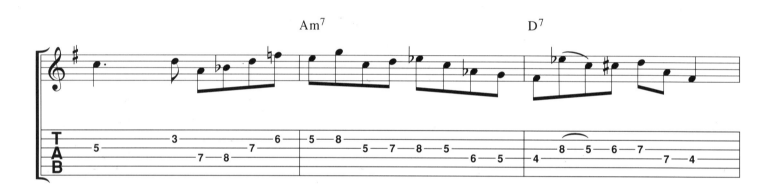

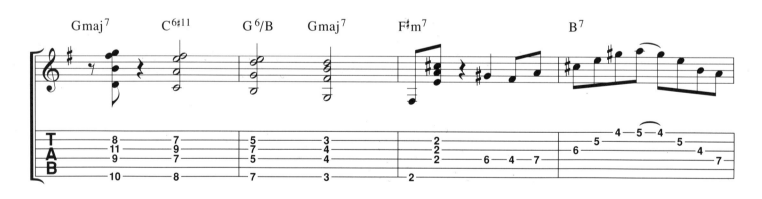

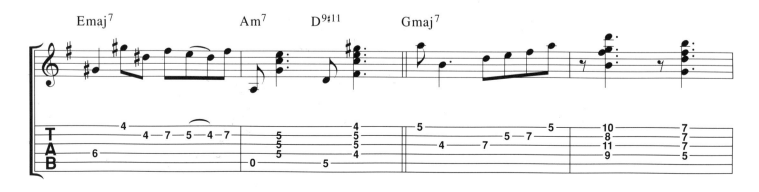

I'm Gettin' Sentimental Over You

Words by Ned Washington. Music by Geo Bassman

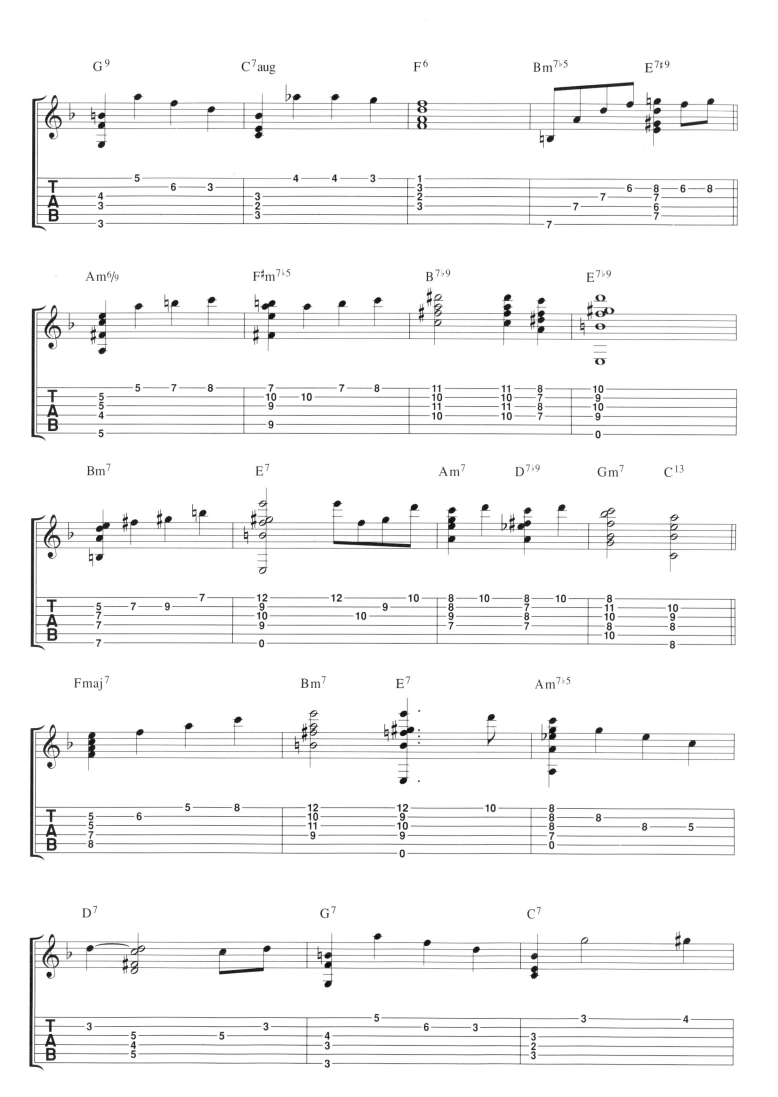

To Coda ⊕

Solo

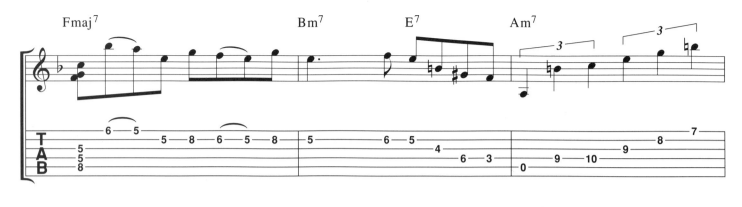

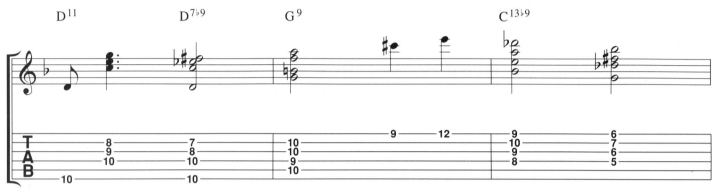

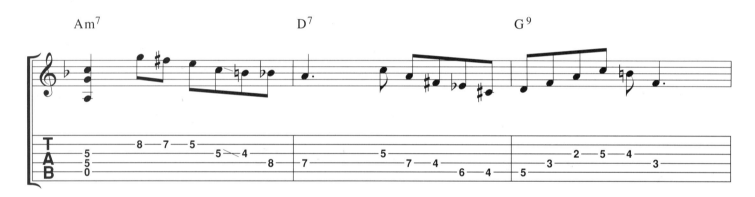

D.%. al Coda

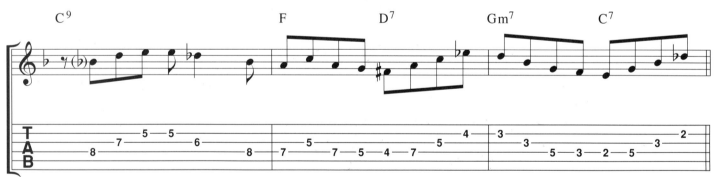

✛ *Coda*

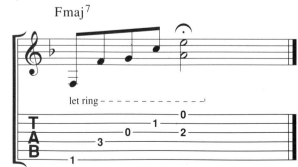

I Wanna Be Around

Words & Music by Johnny Mercer & Sadie Vimmerstedt

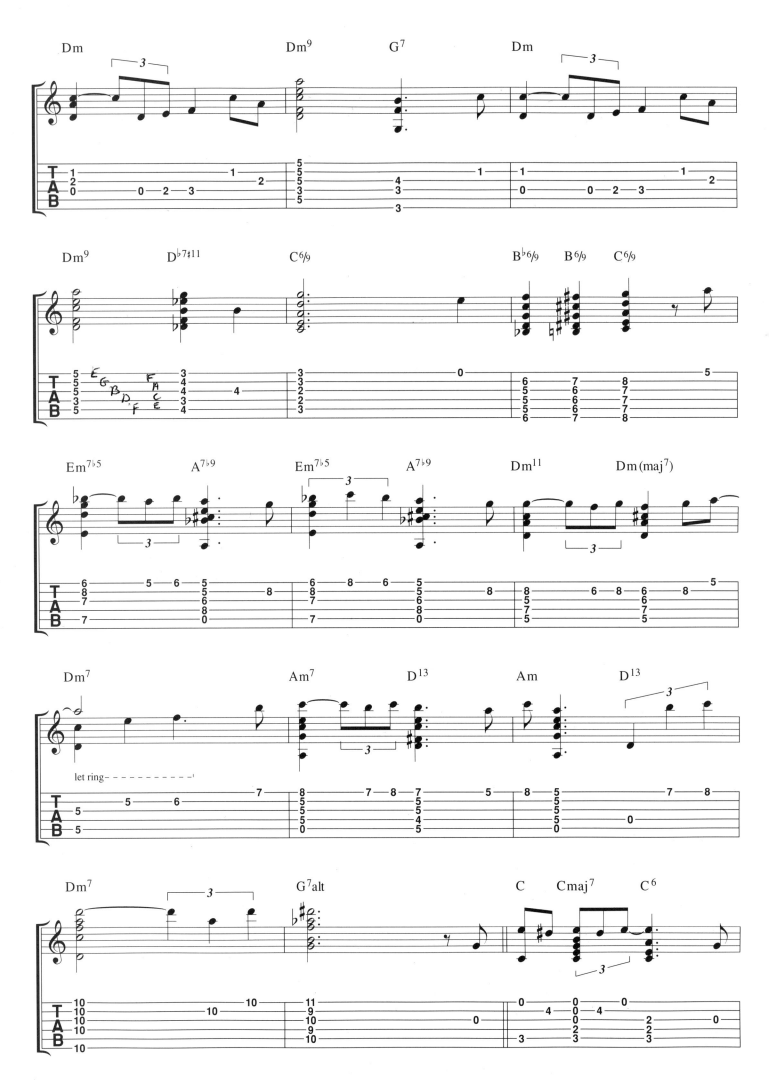

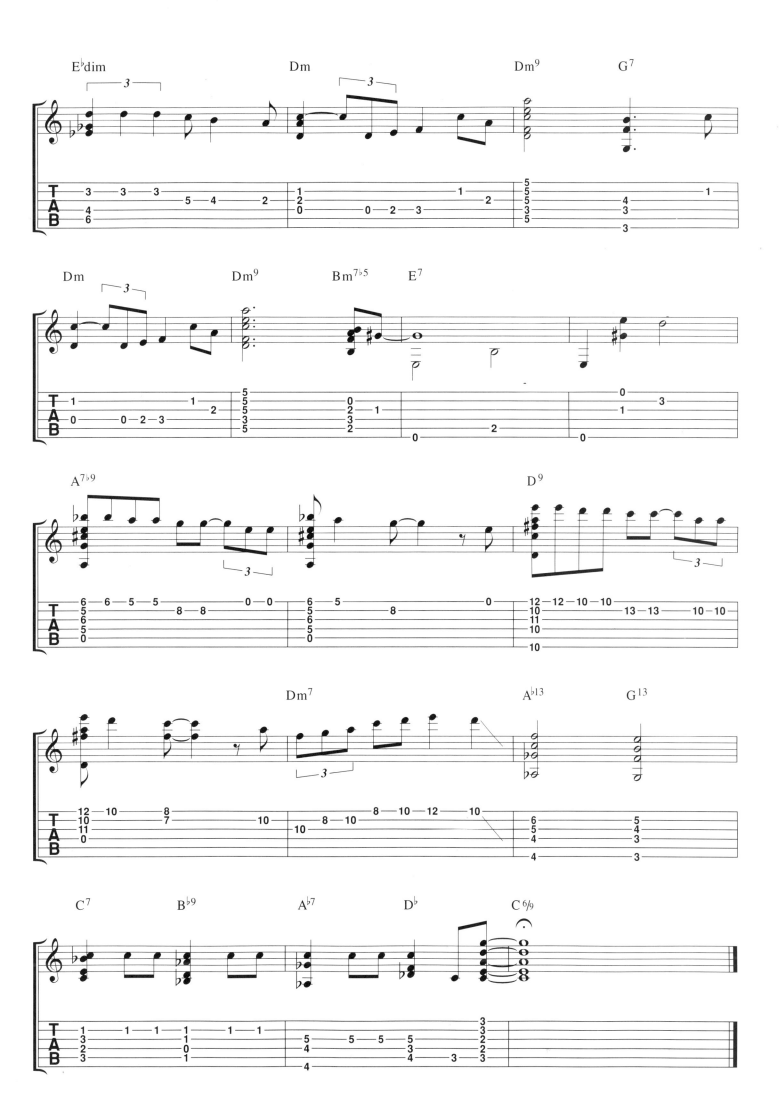

Lazy River

Words & Music by Hoagy Carmichael & Sidney Arodin

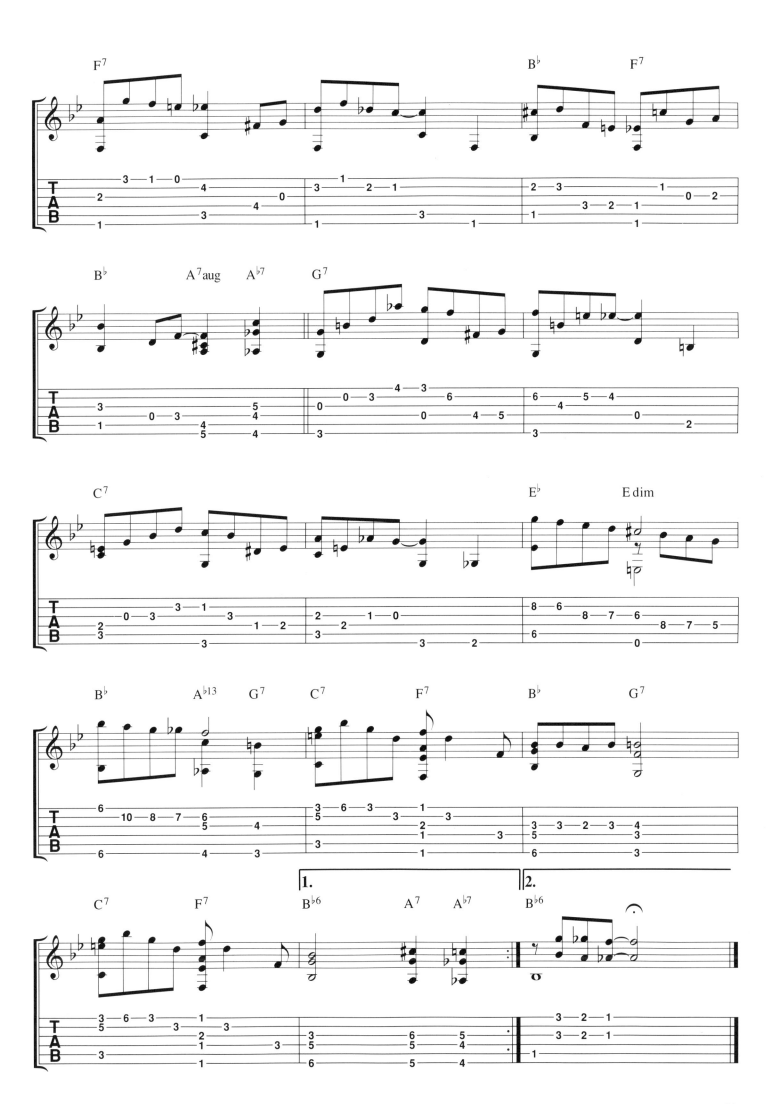

The Nearness Of You

Music by Hoagy Carmichael. Words by Ned Washington

40

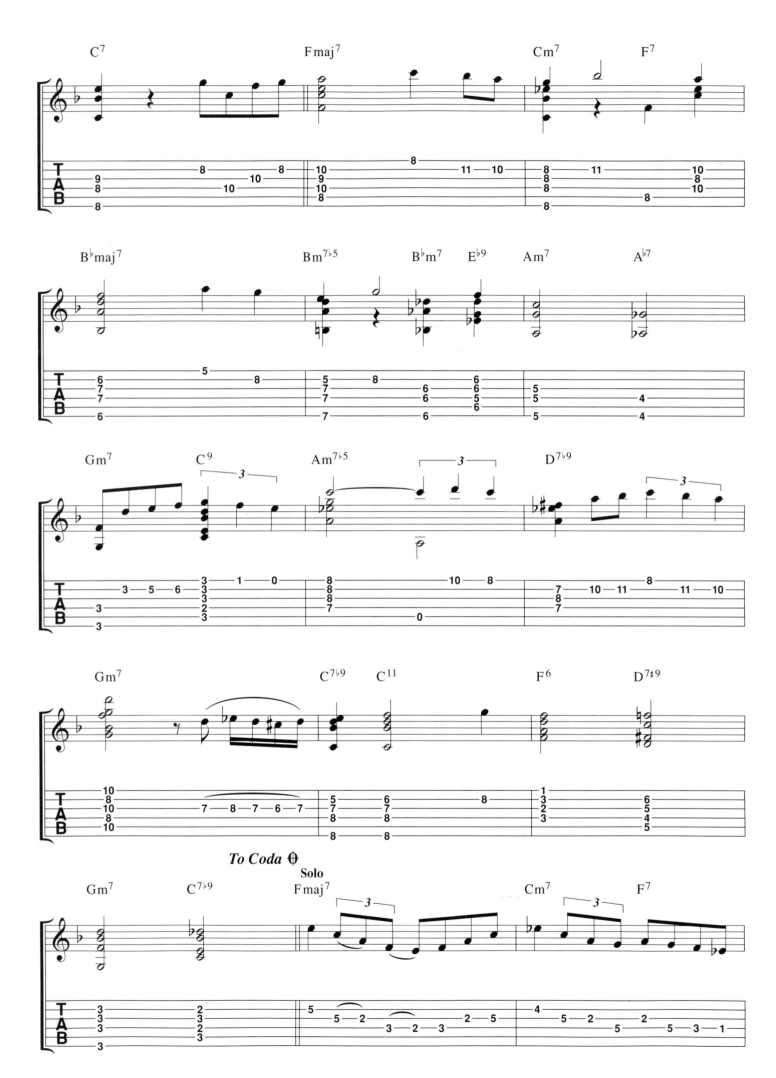

D.%. al Coda

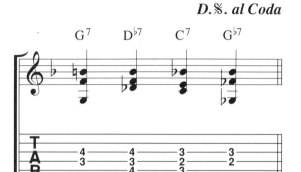

Satin Doll

Words by Johnny Mercer. Music by Duke Ellington & Billy Strayhorn

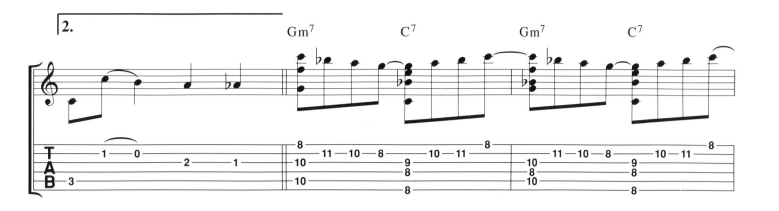

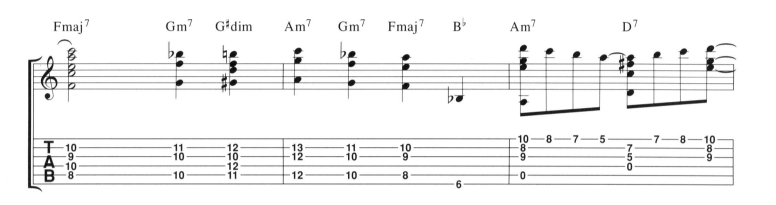

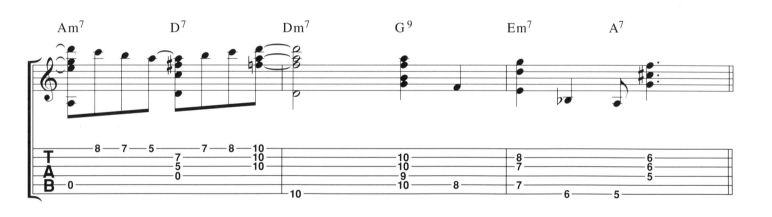

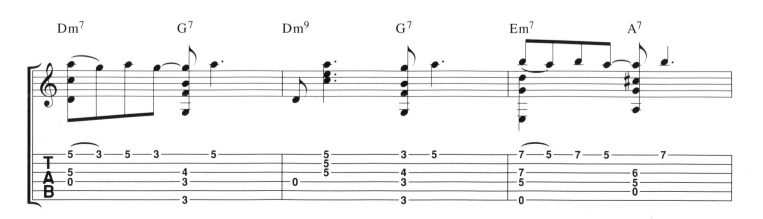

Taking A Chance On Love

Words by John La Touche & Ted Fetter. Music by Vernon Duke

To Coda ⊕

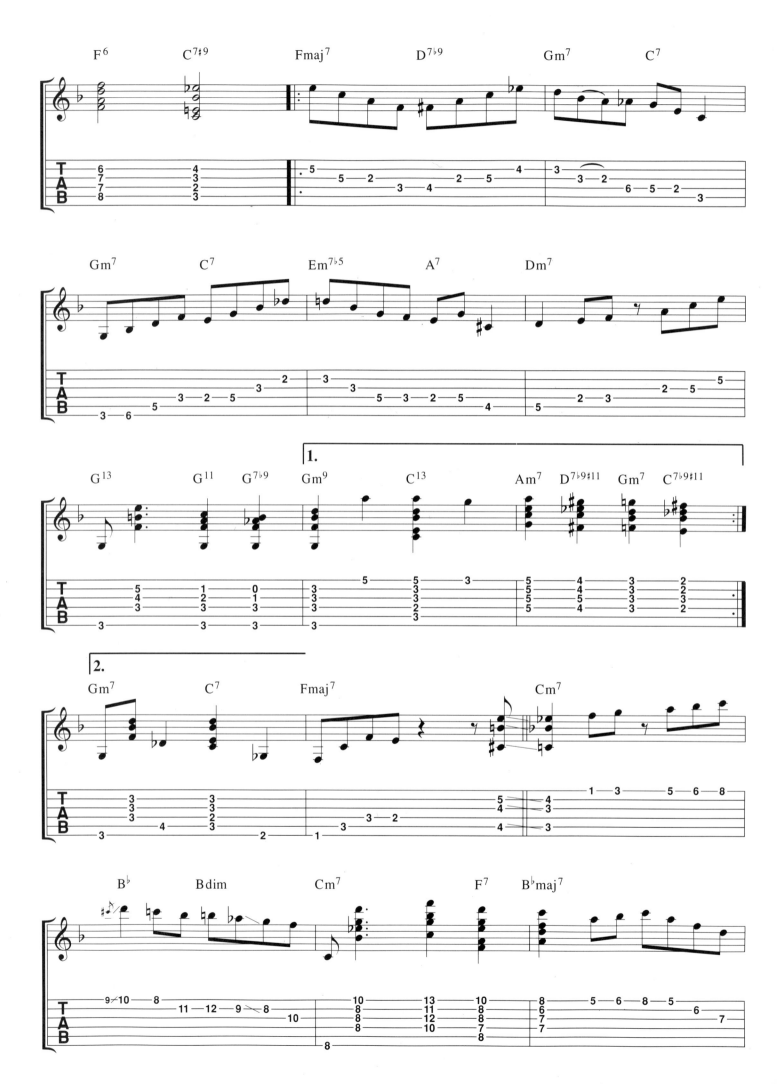

D.℅. al Coda

53

Undecided

Words by Sid Robin. Music by Charles Shavers

Recado Bossa Nova (The Gift)

Words and Music by Djalma Ferreira & Luiz Antonio

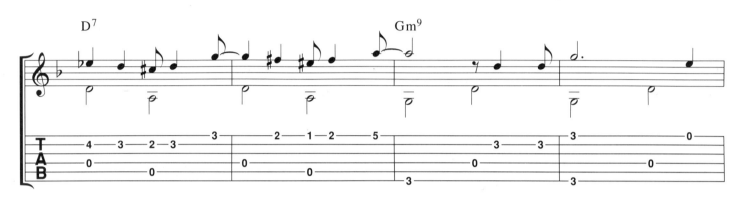

D.𝄋. al Coda

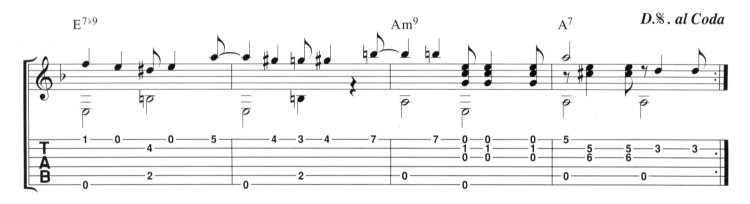

🜨 *Coda*

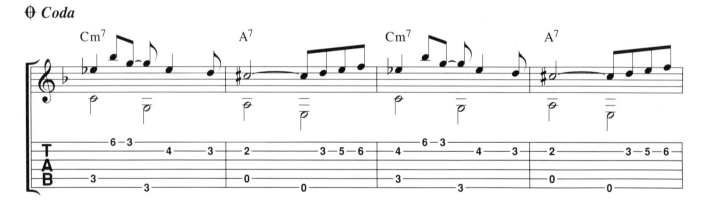

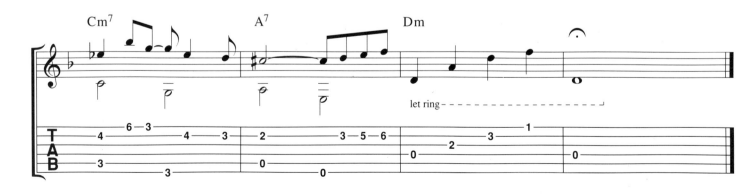

When Sunny Gets Blue

Words by Jack Segal. Music by Marvin Fisher

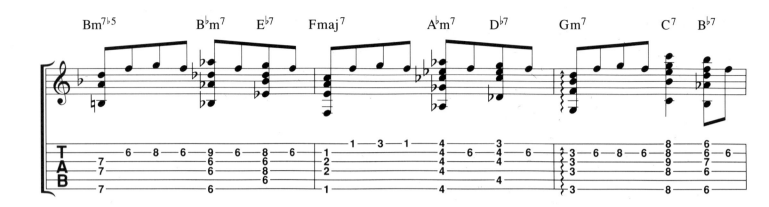

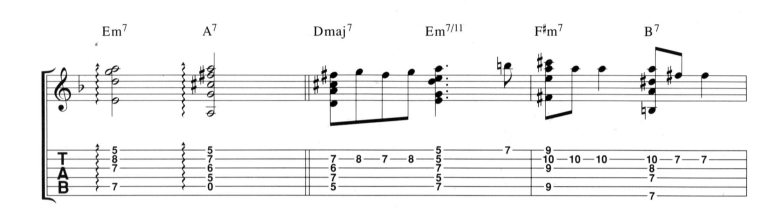

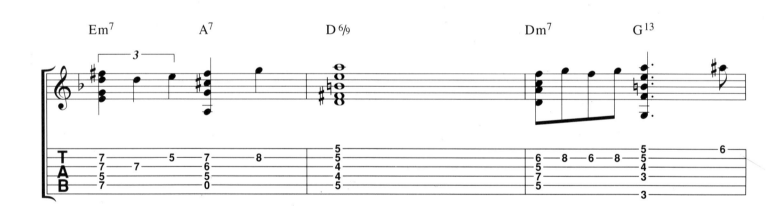

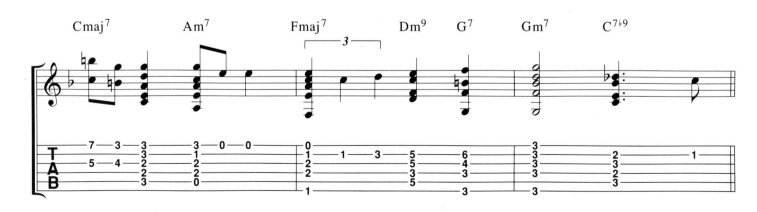

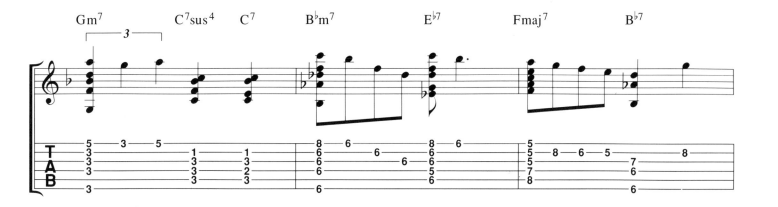

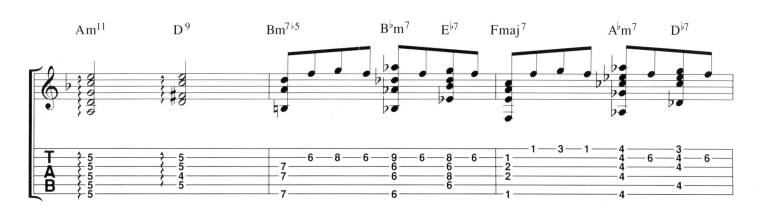

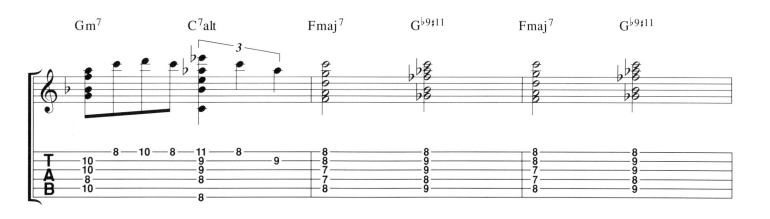

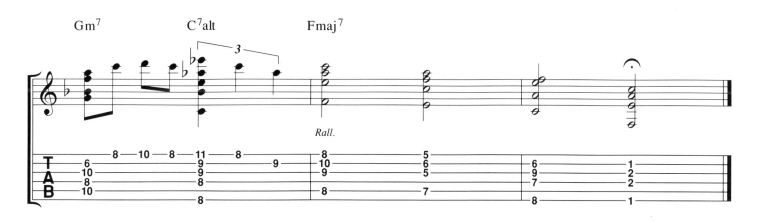